Johnny Birks

M.

Anthony Nelson

Series editor Robert Burton
Diagrams by Jean Vaughan, with permission of the Zoological Society
of London (pp 11 and 12) and Bailliere Tindall (p 21)
Drawings by Graham Allen: 15, 16
Photographs by Johnny Birks: front cover, inside front cover, 7 (left),
inside back cover; Nigel Dunstone: 1, 3; Mark Ireland: 7 (right)

Royalties from this series will go to the Mammal Society

ISBN 0 904614 20 4

Designed by Alan Bartram
Printed by Livesey Ltd, 7 St John's Hill, Shrewsbury

Inside cover
Top: Good mink habitat
Bottom: On a rocky shore

Like some other familiar British mammals, such as the rabbit, grey squirrel and house mouse, the mink is not a native of the British Isles. Its origins lie in North America where wild mink have long been highly prized as the bearers of valuable, glossy fur. Since the late nineteenth century, mink have been bred and raised on 'fur farms', where selective breeding produces pelts of many different colours, shades and textures to suit the whims of the fashion trade. The first American mink were brought to British fur farms in 1929, and all wild mink in Britain today are the descendants of escapees from these fur farms. For this reason they are known as feral mink.

The feral mink has a fearsome reputation as a vicious and wasteful killer of both domestic animals and waterside wildlife. Whether or not it has truly earned this reputation as both an agricultural pest and an 'ecological disaster' is a bone of contention among people familiar with the animal. Whatever the true situation, many mink are killed every year in the name of control or sport. Despite this onslaught, the mink is now common and widespread in Britain, and its vigorous, predatory habits will ensure that it remains a controversial colonist.

The American mink *Mustela vison* is a member of the family Mustelidae, which also contains the skunks, weasels, otters, badgers and martens, as well as the closely related European mink *Mustela lutreola*.

Description

I recall hearing a small boy from Birmingham exclaim 'Look!, a weasel cat!' when he saw his first mink while on holiday in Devon. Such a spontaneous description impressed me, because mink really do resemble an imaginary cross between a black cat and a weasel. Mink are, in fact, much smaller than cats and similar in size to a well-nourished ferret. Male mink are always noticeably larger than females. This sexual dimorphism, with males often weighing twice as much as females, is common among the smaller mustelids such as stoats and weasels.

The mink's body is rather elongate in shape, although less serpentine in its proportions than that of the stoat. The tail represents some 30 per cent of the total length. The legs are relatively short and, despite the aquatic habits, the feet bear only limited webbing between the toes.

Most mink seen in Britain today sport a glossy, dark brown coat of fur, which may appear almost black at times. There are commonly some spots or patches of white fur on the chin, throat, chest and in the groin. Many field guides state categorically that American mink can be distinguished from the European mink by the absence of white fur on the upper lip (the European mink has a noticeable white 'moustache'). This distinction is a very risky one, however, because as many as one American mink in three trapped in Britain has some white fur on its upper lip. Even mink in America may have white on their upper lips, so the phenomenon seen in feral mink need not be regarded as a product of their history of domestication.

Mink moult twice a year. They usually begin to shed their thick, glossy winter coat in April, and replace it with a 'flatter' summer coat which may have a reddish brown tint. They moult again in the autumn, growing their winter coat from September until it becomes what the fur trade calls 'prime' in late November or December.

		Average length of head, body and tail (cm)	Average weight (kg)
Mink	male	60	1.14
	female	51	0.63
Otter	male	119	10.3
	female	104	7.4
Polecat	male	56	1.16
	female	50	0.71
Stoat	male	41	0.32
	female	38	0.21

Measurements of adult mink trapped in Devon, compared with measurements from three other British mustelids.

Because of the mink's recent history of domestication and selective breeding to produce 'fancy' fur colours, throwbacks to these colours still occur commonly in the wild. In Devon about 3 per cent of mink which I live-trapped were a pale silvery-grey colour (called 'silverblue' by the fur trade). In south-west Scotland the proportion of pale-coloured mink was higher: 9 per cent were of the silverblue variety, and a further 2 per cent were a pale silvery-brown colour known as 'sapphire'.

As mink grow older, they often develop areas of white flecking amongst the darker fur around the cheeks and the sides and nape of the neck. These white hairs are thought to grow from the sites of scars received during fighting or mating activity, so that old animals, especially males, may have a grizzled appearance. A few young mink may bear quantities of white flecking throughout the pelt, unlike the scar-induced flecking on the head.

Distribution

In its native North America, the range of the mink stretches from the Arctic wastes of Canada and Alaska down to the swamps of Florida and the arid lands of New Mexico and California. As a result of exports to fur farms and subsequent escapes, American mink now occur in several European countries including Britain, Ireland, France, Spain, Germany, Iceland, Finland and all Scandinavian countries. In addition, over 3,000 American mink were deliberately released, during the 1930s, 1940s and 1950s, in parts of the Soviet Union to establish a source of 'free range' mink fur. Some of these mink have since spread into Poland. These escapes and releases have enabled the feral American mink to colonise much of the old range of the European mink. This species was once common throughout the deciduous forest zones of Europe, but its range is now very much diminished as a result of hunting and trapping.

Spread of mink in Britain

The feral mink has successfully colonised most of Britain and Ireland in less than 30 years. The establishment of a feral population, breeding in the wild, was first confirmed in July 1956, when a female and kits were sighted on the River Teign in Devon. During the late 1950s and early 1960s similar populations became established and flourished in Hampshire, Wiltshire, Sussex, Lancashire and West Yorkshire.

This early, patchy colonisation tended to reflect the general distribution of escapes (or deliberate release) of mink in areas liberally supplied with mink farms. In 1962, however, all mink farms were brought under legislative control by the Mink (Importation and Keeping) Order, made under the Destructive Imported Animals Act, 1932. Fewer escapes occurred subsequently, and the spread of feral mink tended to continue through the expansion of existing populations rather than as a result of fresh escapes

During the 1960s, the Ministry of Agriculture, Fisheries and Food trapped over 5,000 mink in England and Wales, but the animals continued to spread and the battle to control them was lost. By the early 1970s feral mink had been recorded in every county. However, there are still some areas where they are scarce or absent in Britain. In Wales, for example, mink are scarce in the north-west, and mid-Wales is still being colonised. Rivers in the south-west of the country, such as the Usk, Tywi and Teifi are well-populated with mink, however. In Scotland, most of the mainland south of the Great Glen is fully colonised by mink, while their distribution to the north is patchy. Some of the western islands, such as Lewis and Harris in the Outer Hebrides and Arran in the south, also have mink. In England, the south and west are well colonised, while the midlands are rather patchily occupied. In the north, Lancashire and the three counties of Yorkshire are well colonised, while mink are still expanding their range in parts of Cumbria, Durham and Northumberland.

In Ireland, feral mink probably occur in every county (with the possible exception of Galway), but their distribution remains sparse and restricted in many southern and western counties such as Mayo, Clare, Limerick, Kerry and Cork. The best colonised areas are the North of Ireland, especially County Donegal, and the midlands and eastern seaboard.

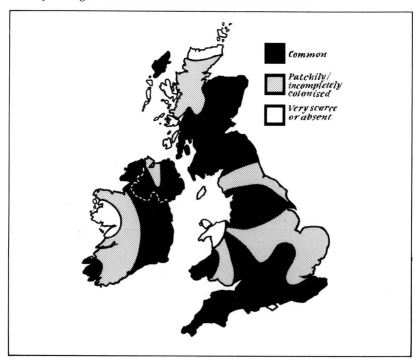

Legend:
Common
Patchily/incompletely colonised
Very scarce or absent

Left: Footprints in the sand show the mink's five digits.
Right: A mink has bounded over the snow.

Signs

The only reliable indication of the presence of feral mink, apart from sightings of the animal itself, is the discovery of footprints or droppings (called scats). However, caution should be exercised in areas where polecats are common (as in parts of Wales) because the signs left by the two species are virtually indistinguishable.

Mink footprints are best searched for in wet mud along the edges of lakes and streams. Except in very soft mud, prints usually show only four of the five pointed toes, radiating forwards from the central pad. Claw marks are often visible at the ends of the toe pads. The prints of adult male mink tend to be larger (over 2.75 centimetres) than those of adult females (less than 2.75 centimetres), so it is frequently possible to guess at the sex of the animal. Confusion may occur in summer, when the prints of young males may be the same size as those of adult females.

Mink scats are usually deposited on prominent objects in the waterside habitat, such as rocks, fallen tree trunks, bridge bases and grassy mounds. Otters choose similar sites for their droppings (called spraints), but the two can be distinguished with the help of a good nose and a little experience. Mink scats are cylindrical, 5–8 centimetres long and usually less than 1 centimetre diameter. The ends are usually tapered. The scats' colour tends to vary with the freshness and the nature of their contents: many are a dark

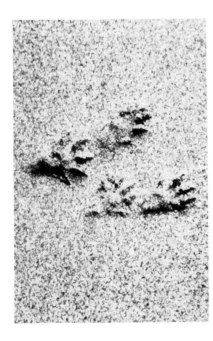

7

greeny-brown, approaching black; much paler scats arise when a mink has been feeding on a pale coloured bird, or on crabs or crayfish. Fresh mink scats have a quite unpleasant smell due to the covering of jelly-like secretion from the scent glands. By comparison, fresh otter spraints have a much more acceptable sweet, musky smell, and are more variable in size. Also, they are generally much less compact and rarely retain a neat cylindrical shape.

Where mink live

Mink have a preference for living by the waterside. In Britain they may be seen on every kind of waterway, hunting along tiny acid upland streams or broad lowland rivers and canals. They may visit ponds, lakes and reservoirs, and are commonly seen in estuaries (sometimes making a home on moored boats if natural den sites are scarce) and even on rocky coastlines. They may even be found inhabiting rivers and canals on the outskirts of cities, provided there is sufficient bankside cover to support prey and to afford shelter and den sites. Travelling mink certainly pass through quite large cities by following waterways. One mink which I trapped and ear-tagged on the River Exe just South of Exeter was shot some 5 kilometres to the north of the city two weeks later.

Mink are often seen well away from water, especially at those times of year when rutting males are searching for females (February-March) or when young mink have left their birthplaces to search for vacant territories (August-September). Mink are less closely tied to aquatic habitats than are otters, so they are capable of living for long periods away from waterways, provided prey such as rabbits, small mammals and birds are available.

8

Numbers

Mink are more numerous in certain types of habitat. The numbers in an area are determined largely by the size of territory which each mink defends against other individuals. Mink are scarcer where larger territories are needed in poor habitat because food is scarce. Poor habitats for mink are those waters where bankside cover is thin or absent, as on many artificial reservoirs, or where prey are scarce as in many acid upland streams. In poor habitats, mink may hold territories covering up to 5 kilometres of river. Where food is very scarce, the length of river mink would need to defend in order to feed themselves in the long term may be too great to make the effort worthwhile, so they adopt a drifting or 'transient' lifestyle, wandering along watercourses until they find a more suitable vacant stretch.

The best habitat for mink in fresh waters is found on lakes, slow-flowing streams and small rivers with a high nutrient content and an abundance of cover next to the water's edge. In these conditions food is plentiful and mink may occupy territories as little as 1 kilometre in length. Mink seem especially fond of waterways fringed with reedbeds, since these are good places to hunt waterfowl and small fish. One mink which I studied occupied an area of marsh, stream and reedbed of only 9 hectares. If such habitat occurred more extensively in Britain, mink might be found living at densities comparable to those observed on the best marshes in Iowa and Dakota in the United States, where as many as 8–12 adult mink may pack into each square kilometre.

Because the movements of transient mink, searching for mates or vacant territories, tend to occur along waterways, these 'passers-by' often give an exaggerated impression of the number of mink actually resident on a stretch of stream or river. I know of gamekeepers who, having caught a dozen adult mink on a half-mile stretch of river over a week's trapping, proudly announce that they have 'cleaned out' the colony that was living there. Mink are not colonial, however, so most of the dozen trapped would have been simply passing through the territory occupied by a single resident.

Coastal habitat where rockpools provide abundant seafood is even better than fresh water, and mink are more numerous here than anywhere else in Britain. In our study of coast-living mink in south-west Scotland, we have found densities as high as one or two adult mink per kilometre of coastline in some areas. Here, the mink seem to prefer gently-sloping, scrub-covered coasts with broad rocky shores; cliffs and shingle beaches are less popular as hunting grounds.

Very little is known about the natural causes of death in feral mink. A great number are trapped and killed by farmers and gamekeepers, and some are hunted and killed by packs of minkhounds during the summer months. Apart from Man, however, the mink has no significant predators. Large birds of prey, such as golden eagles and harriers, may take them occasionally, and I know of one instance of a badger killing a young mink. Otters have been known to eat mink in Russia, and this led to concern that otters might reduce the numbers of valuable fur-bearing mink which the Russians were trying to maintain in the wild! But, by and large, mink numbers seem to be regulated by their own territorial behaviour rather than by the influence of other species. Those mink which fail to win a territory have their chances of survival greatly reduced, and many probably die of starvation or disease.

Activity and behaviour

Studying the movements and behaviour of elusive species like the mink is made possible by two marking techniques. First, animals are trapped and fitted with numbered metal ear-tags. The pattern of recaptures of eartagged mink during a live-trapping study reveals which mink are residents on a stretch of river and which are merely passing through. It also gives an idea of the density of residents, the size of their territories and the extent that they overlap, and the duration of tenure. Second, much more detailed information on movements and behaviour can be collected by radio-tracking. This involves fitting a small radio transmitter to the mink, and subsequently locating the signal by means of a receiver and aerial. In this way it is possible to locate animals and their hunting and resting places. Also, the pattern of the signal received gives an indication of whether the animal is resting or active.

Mink are solitary animals as a rule, each defending a territory against others of the species. Only at certain times of the year are mink commonly seen together. In mid-summer family parties of mother and kits hunt the waterside, and in early spring males may be seen fighting or pursuing females. Territorial encounters between mink may occur at any time of year, but they are most common in late summer and autumn when young mink disperse and competition for territories is greatest.

Although mink occupy separate territories, those of males and females may overlap considerably. This may benefit males in the mating season, since they will know where best to look for the females and so be able to check their reproductive condition frequently. The territories of two mink of the same sex rarely overlap to any great extent.

Mink territories tend to be long and thin in shape, because they extend along rivers, lake edges or the seashore. Most activity is concentrated within 50 metres of the water's edge, but mink sometimes hunt 400 metres or more away from water if terrestrial prey such as rabbits are abundant. Male mink are more likely to be found hunting away from water because their larger size makes them better rabbit-catchers than females.

Like many other carnivores, mink spend most of their time asleep or resting. Radio-collared mink on the Galloway coast were found to spend 84 per cent of their time in dens, sleeping, grooming or eating food which they had carried home. Dens are, therefore, an important component of the waterside habitat from the mink's point of view. An analysis of the dens

The home range of an adult mink on the River Teign in Devon, indicated by dots. The nine dens (A to I) are marked X. This mink fed mainly on small fish, and like most mink her dens tended to be close to her favourite hunting areas (shaded).

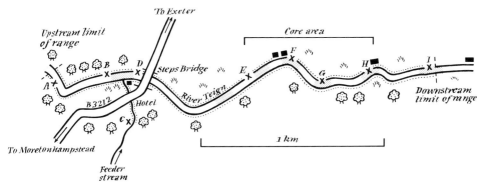

used by radio-collared mink in Devon revealed that water-side trees were the most popular sites, especially oaks and sycamores with cavernous, eroded root systems, or old willows with hollow trunks or branches. Rabbit burrows were often used as dens, usually after the original owners had been eaten!

Mink show ingenuity in their choice of dens where suitable sites are in short supply (they rarely dig their own dens, preferring to use a ready-made hole). One mink which I studied in Devon slept in an old woodpigeon nest, 5 metres up an ivy-covered willow tree, because the area was too marshy for comfortable dens at ground level. Another slept in a tea-chest in a barn next to a butcher's shop and one family even lived under the boards of a raised birdwatchers' causeway through a reedbed.

Mink are tirelessly inquisitive and often surprisingly unafraid of Man. This may lead to a mink's downfall, because it is as likely to approach and investigate a man with a gun as it is to run away from him. It is even easy to coax a mink out of its den by making squeaking noises at the entrance.

Within its territory each mink may have a number of dens in regular use at any one time (except breeding females which tend to use a single den during May and June). The average number of dens regularly used by radio-collared mink in Devon was six, ranging from two to ten. Dens are spaced at intervals of 200–500 metres along the river or shore. The longer the mink's territory, the more dens it tends to use. This pattern reflects the awkward shape of a long, thin territory which cannot easily be defended or exploited from a single central den. Because the most important boundaries are at the furthest extremities, and because the foraging areas are strung out in a line, a mink needs refuges along the whole length of territory.

Mink visit their territory boundaries regularly, and make occasional excursions to check up on neighbouring territory-holders. They exploit their foraging areas on a loosely rotational basis, but there is generally one patch which is favoured above the rest at any one point in time. This core area is usually a patch in which a certain type of prey is seasonally abundant, such

The pattern of a mink's movements. Note the core area based around the dens F to H and the patrolling to the extremities of the territory.

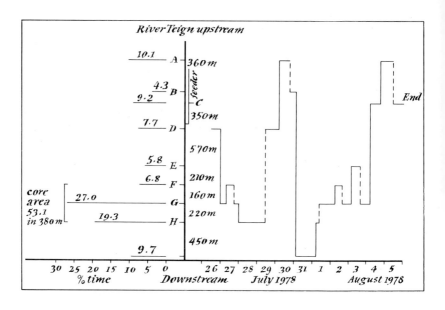

as a good 'crabby' stretch of shore, a 'rabbity' hedgerow or a chain of pools in a stream with plenty of eels.

When a mink is spotted hunting along a river bank or sea shore, it gives an impression of great energy and 'busy-ness' as it quarters the ground, exploring every nook, cranny and pool. For hunting fish, a mink often chooses a good viewpoint overlooking a favourite pool, and peers intently into the water below. It may dive in and search for prey underwater, or it may spy a fish from above and give chase directly it enters the water. It is likely that mink use their whiskers, as otters do, when searching for prey in murky water. Prey caught in the water are carried to land before being consumed.

Although mink may be seen hunting at any time, most activity occurs at night or around dawn and dusk. Radio-tracking studies have shown that each individual mink tends to have its own particular rhythm of activity, which is often dictated by the prey's behaviour. One female mink which I studied left her waterside den to dive for small fish roughly every six hours, with each hunting trip lasting only about 20–30 minutes. She was evidently exploiting an abundant and predictable food supply close to her den, which enabled her to pop out and feed as the need arose.

Mink which hunt adult rabbits may go for a day or two without hunting, because a rabbit carcass can keep a mink in meat for at least two days. On the coast foraging activity may be influenced by the tidal cycle, because mink can hunt most profitably on the shore at low tide, whatever the time of day or night. This does not apply to all animals, however, for some seem to be influenced more by the day-night cycle than the tides. Mink are, therefore, highly unpredictable, and it is unwise to generalise beyond the statement that a mink hunts when it feels it needs to!

Apart from the smaller items, prey are usually carried to a nearby refuge or den at the end of a successful hunt, to be eaten in comfort and safety, or stored for future use. Mink may build up sizeable caches of food, although this habit is apparently less common in Britain than in parts of its native range where severe winters make such behaviour especially valuable. The accumulations of prey and remains at mink dens can yield useful information on diet, especially if they allow the identification of species which cannot be distinguished from remains in droppings.

Senses and communication

Studies of the mink's eyesight indicate that it is only moderate in air and even poorer underwater. Neither is the hearing especially acute, but the sense of smell is excellent, and mink rely on this sense above all others when hunting on land. Underwater, mink use their eyes, and probably also their whiskers when searching nooks and crannies for prey.

Mink are comparatively silent animals, only calling during close encounters with each other, or when cornered by a dangerous predator such as Man. During unfriendly encounters between two animals, a limited range of screeches, hisses and screams may be heard as dominance is established. A cornered mink, for example one caught in a trap, will emit a loud and ear-piercing shriek if threatened. This is a form of 'defensive threat' which serves to warn the intimidator that 'I will attack you if you come too close'. Mink also make a noise which has been described as a chuckle (like gentle laughter suppressed by a closed mouth). This is heard most often when the male gives vent to his arousal by 'chuckling' as he pursues a female on heat. Young mink often squeak repetitively as they follow their mother through unfamiliar habitat on their first hunting trips (see p. 22).

Much of the communication between mink is probably achieved indirectly, by the release of long-lasting scent-marks which contain information about their producers. Scent may be deposited in several ways. Droppings for example, are coated in a jelly-like secretion from the proctodeal glands which open into the rectum. Sometimes blobs of this strong-smelling jelly are deposited in the absence of droppings. Different secretions, from the anal glands, may be forced out as a jelly smear by the process of 'anal drag', in which the mink rubs its anus over the ground while in a sitting position. Mink may also deposit scent from glands in the skin by rubbing the chest and throat over objects such as tree roots, logs and rocks.

Chemical analysis of the mink's anal scent gland secretions has revealed a range of high molecular weight compounds which are specific to individuals. This suggests that mink may be able to recognise each other from their scent alone. Scent marks may also carry information on the age, territorial status and reproductive condition of the marker.

Scent marks tend to be deposited deliberately in prominent places within the home range so as to maximise both their active range and the chances of other mink encountering them. They undoubtedly contribute to the maintenance of the territorial system as a consequence of their general function as suppliers of information about individuals.

As well as producing fairly long-lasting scents, which may convey information for several weeks if weather conditions are favourable, mink also produce more volatile substances. A frightened or aggressively aroused mink is capable of producing a very powerful, acrid stench in a matter of seconds. When combined with a defensive 'screaming fit', this stink may serve as a skunk-style deterrent to predators, including human ones! It could also have an intimidatory function during aggressive encounters between mink.

Food

The carnivorous mink is often described as a generalist predator, because of the lack of specialization in its hunting behaviour. It is very much a 'Jack of all trades', hunting prey on the ground, down burrows, underwater and occasionally even up trees. Mammals, birds, fish and invertebrates all feature in the diet, and the relative proportions of each vary both with the habitat and the time of year. Mallards, frogs, rabbits, crayfish, field voles, moorhens, eels, common rats and roach are all taken by mink on lowland lakes and rivers, for example.

The most important mammal prey is rabbits, which are normally killed underground in their burrows. Where rabbits are numerous they may make up more than 50 per cent of the mink's diet in the summer months. Since a fully grown rabbit is normally larger than a mink, it is a fairly formidable prey to tackle in the tight confines of a burrow. Male mink are strong enough to overpower adult rabbits, but the smaller females seem to prefer less risky foods and only prey heavily on rabbits in summer, when young ones are abundant.

Several species of small mammals, such as voles, mice and rats, are preyed upon by mink in small numbers; shrews are occasionally taken, but they may be killed and left uneaten because of their unpleasant taste. Brown hares are occasionally killed by mink but, in view of their large size, it is likely that only young or sick animals are taken.

Birds may make up over 30 per cent of the mink's diet, and predation is especially high in summer, when fledglings and young waterfowl are vulnerable. The presence of shell remains in droppings suggests that eggs are also eaten. Small woodland birds and gamebirds are taken by mink, but waterbirds, especially coots and moorhens, are the most important group to

mink, often representing over 80 per cent of birds eaten on lowland waterways.

Of the birds eaten by coastal mink (16 per cent of their total diet in one study), seabirds such as gulls and waders account for 53 per cent. It is not unusual to find the oiled remains of gulls or auks at mink dens on the coast, suggesting that mink often take them as carrion.

A wide range of fish species are caught by mink, although the slower-swimming coarse fish, especially eels, are preferred. Mink can swim underwater well, but they rarely stay submerged for more than 10 seconds when diving for fish, so shallow water is preferred for hunting. Although mink prefer fresh-killed meat, I have known them to eat quite putrid carcasses of salmon long after they had died following spawning. Healthy adult salmon are too large for mink to catch, and most fish caught by mink are less than 15 centimetres long, although eels of up to 30 centimetres are commonly taken. Mink are adept at winkling small blennies, butterfish, rocklings and scorpionfish out of rockpools at low tide. These rockpool fish may represent a quarter of the mink's diet in coastal habitat.

Amphibians such as frogs are only occasionally eaten by mink, and there is only one record of a snake. Of the invertebrates taken, only two species are

16

The diet of male and female mink (determined from scats of known animals), on a stretch of Scottish coast. Females take smaller prey, mainly from the shore. Males rely heavily on large terrestrial species.

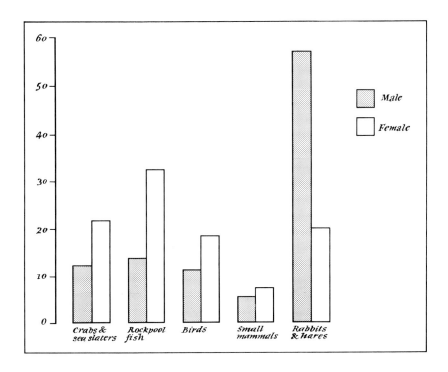

commonly eaten. Shore crabs are eaten by mink on the coast, especially in the summer months when the crabs are moulting and mating in rockpools on the shore. In some hard-water rivers crayfish are common, and chunks of their tough armour of exoskeleton are often found in mink droppings. Sometimes coastal mink eat sea slaters (like large amphibious woodlice), which they catch among rocks and seaweed at the top of the shore. Earthworms are occasionally eaten, and at least one brave animal raided a bees' nest to eat the larvae, pupae, adults and wax!

Is there a mink problem?

Apart from the feral cat, the mink is the only foreign carnivore to have become widely established in the British Isles. Introduced species have often caused problems, both ecological and agricultural, in their new homes, so it is sensible to ask two questions about the presence of feral mink in Britain. First, what effect do mink have upon domestic stock and the populations of mammals, birds, fish and invertebrates on which they prey? Second, do mink compete for food with native carnivores, such as the otter, stoat or polecat? A series of research projects has come up with some answers.

*The composition of the mink's diet may vary considerably between
habitats, depending on the range of prey available.*

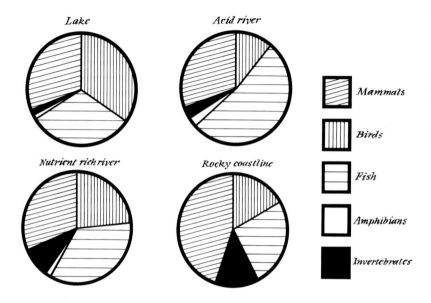

Lake

Acid river

Nutrient rich river

Rocky coastline

Mammals

Birds

Fish

Amphibians

Invertebrates

Mink will prey upon domestic stock, but only if they are given the
opportunity. Chickens and ducks which are badly housed or 'free range' are
at risk, as are fish in fish farms and collections of pinioned waterfowl. In most
cases, losses to mink can be avoided by good husbandry, involving secure
mink-proof housing or fencing, and strategic trapping of mink near sites at
risk.

The importance of domestic species as the prey of mink was put in
perspective by a study of the diet of mink in south-west England. Analysis of
685 droppings showed that chickens and gamebirds made up less than 1 per
cent of the total diet. Reports of mink killing small dogs, cats, lambs, and
even calves, occasionally appear in the newspapers. If such events ever truly
happen, they can be regarded as rare and exceptional. Mink prefer small
prey, although they will fiercely defend themselves against larger animals if
they are threatened.

The impact of feral mink upon British agriculture is negligible when
viewed alongside economic pests like the rabbit, woodpigeon and common
rat. While it may be fair to describe the mink as a minor nuisance, it has
clearly not earned the title of serious agricultural pest.

The analysis of mink droppings and stomach contents has revealed that a
very wide range of prey is taken. Some people argue that such a vigorous,
all-pervading predator must have a devastating effect upon the fragile
balance of wetland habitats. We should not forget, however, that predation is
a normal part of nature, so long as it is not excessive and likely to deplete
prey populations. Is mink predation excessive? Has it led to the serious

decline in numbers of any species in Britain over the last 20 years? I believe the answer is a qualified NO.

Studies of prey populations have revealed that they are capable of withstanding mink predation in their optimum habitats. Moorhens and coots, for example, are preyed upon heavily by mink in areas of reedbed surrounding Slapton Ley, a lake in South Devon, yet they are still very abundant there. However, declines in moorhen numbers have been noticed on some waters where the habitat is less suitable for the birds (so-called marginal habit). Similarly, declines in numbers of water voles on some rivers may or may not be due to mink predation. The picture is complicated by the fact that water voles have disappeared from some rivers where mink are absent, while maintaining their numbers on other rivers where mink are present.

The explanation for the mink's overall slight impact upon the 'ecological balance' seems to lie in its tendency to concentrate upon common, easily available prey, while always being ready to turn to a number of alternatives should the favoured species become less abundant. By exploiting prey species only when they are abundant, the mink do not concentrate on one particular type of prey until its numbers are seriously diminished. Furthermore, this habit of varying the diet to match local and seasonal changes in prey numbers goes a long way towards explaining the mink's success.

The same may not be said, however, at small offshore islands where communities of potential prey species have developed in the absence of mammalian predators. For example, colonies of ground-nesting birds on islands are liable to suffer from the introduction of mink or any other terrestrial predator. Some ground-nesting colonial birds such as gulls mount effective anti-predator actions in the form of mobbing. One island colony of herring gulls which I have visited regularly continues to expand despite the presence of a female mink and her young near the colony every summer.

The second question concerns the effect on native carnivores. The mink has often been blamed for driving out the otter, even though the latter is a much bigger animal and a superior fisherman. Although the otter is very much scarcer than it was before the mink colonised British rivers, a close examination of hunting records revealed that the decline in numbers started in the late 1950s over most of England and Wales – well before the mink had become widely established. Chemical pollution, particularly the pesticide Dieldrin, is thought to be the most likely explanation for the otter's demise. Nevertheless, there remained the possibility that mink might compete with otters for food. Studies of the diet of mink and otters suggest an overlap of up to 30–40 per cent. Fish made up 63 per cent of shared food in one study. Since otters are highly specialised at catching fish, they would be likely to out-compete mink when fish are in short supply.

Mink live side by side with otters on many waterways in Britain, and with other carnivores such as the stoat and polecat on land. This situation seems to be an example of a generalist predator (the 'Jack of all trades' mink) coexisting with more specialised predators which are all 'masters' of their own particular 'trade'. Were mink ever forced to compete directly with specialist predators for scarce prey they would certainly lose out. They avoid this competition by always choosing plentiful prey and quickly switching from one prey to another when necessary.

The absence of any obvious competition between the feral mink and native carnivores suggests that it has filled an ecological niche which was vacant in Britain until now. This is the very niche, perhaps, that the European mink would have occupied if it had managed to colonise the British Isles at the end of the Ice Age.

Breeding

Mink breed once a year. Mating occurs in February and March when males travel extensively to find and mate with as many females as they can. Females are on heat for about three weeks, and each female may be mated by several males during this period. There is no pair bond and their 'free-for-all' mating behaviour is described as promiscuous. Some males actually leave their territories in search of receptive females and never return. Others simply extend their movements around the home base.

Male mink are very aggressive towards each other during the mating season, often fighting each other on sight, even when there is no female in the vicinity. These fights look and sound furious, with much rolling, biting and screaming, but they rarely lead to serious injury because the bites are aimed at the tough, thick skin around the head and neck. Fights end when the weaker animal starts to squeak pathetically to indicate submission, and the winner usually lets it flee. Fights between equally matched males have been seen to last up to 12 minutes, leaving both animals panting and exhausted at the end.

When a male mink finds a female on heat, he may try to guard her against other males for a few days before moving on. When mink mate, the male grips the female by the scruff of the neck with his teeth, causing her to scream pitifully. Because females may be mated several times in this manner, often by a succession of different males, an unpleasant open wound appears on the nape of the neck. These wounds often become infected, and its not unknown for females to die as a result of mating injuries or exhaustion. During copulation the male maintains his hold on the female's neck, grips her body with his forelegs, and curves his rear end round and beneath hers. The pair lie on their sides in this position for an hour or more, with the male thrusting violently at intervals.

Pregnancy lasts an average of 51 days, although the duration is quite variable (40–75 days) due to the process of delayed implantation. In Britain, most feral mink give birth in late April or early May. The pregnant female

Frequency of dive durations. When chasing small fish underwater, mink tend to give up sooner if the chase began as a result of an underwater search (search chase). However, if the fish was spotted from out of the water beforehand (dive chase), mink are able to spend more of their limited underwater time giving chase before they run out of breath.

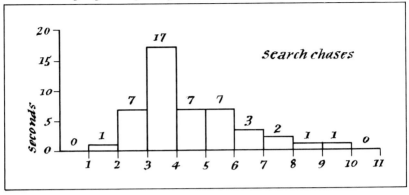

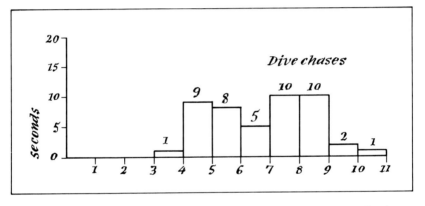

selects a breeding den during April. This may be in a hollow tree, pile of rocks or rabbit burrow. The kits are born in a nest of vegetation collected from around the den by their mother.

Usually four to six young are born. They are blind, deaf, bald and helpless, and weigh about 5 grams. After a week or two they develop a thin, silvery coat of fine hair which lengthens and thickens at about four weeks to produce the dark grey, soft juvenile coat. For the first month or so the mother spends a great deal of her time with the kits, venturing out of the den only briefly to feed. By the end of May the still-blind kits weigh about 100 grams and are much more mobile, often wandering towards the den entrance, only to be dragged back to the safety of the nest by their mother. I have even seen a nervous mother mink, in mid-July, trying to drag her almost full-grown young ones back to their den by the scruffs of their necks, when danger threatened, even though they were larger than she was!

The young minks' eyes open in the first or second week of June, when they are about five weeks old. Weaning starts at about this age, when the kits first suck on flesh brought into the den by their mother. By mid-June the kits are

21

allowed out of the den under the close supervision of their mother. By the end of June they begin to accompany her on foraging trips away from the den. They are still very vulnerable at this stage, and all stay very close to their mother, often squeaking repeatedly as she guides them along the riverbank or seashore. This squeaking probably serves to keep the family together in dense waterside vegetation. When a kit becomes separated from the rest of the family, it begins to squeak louder and more rapidly (200 squeaks per minute), thereby alerting its mother who comes to the rescue.

During July the kits become bolder and more adventurous. They replace their milk teeth with the sharp adult dentition, and grow their glossy adult fur. The difference in size between males and females is obvious by mid-July, and young of both sexes may weigh more than their scrawny mother. Since adult male mink play no part in the rearing of young, breeding females have to manage alone. The strain of catching sufficient prey for themselves and their ever-hungry kits commonly leads to loss of condition, so that breeding females may lose as much as one fifth of their weight by the end of July.

Young mink learn to hunt around the home territory with their mother until about the third week of July, when they are about ten weeks old. They then cease to depend on their mother for food. An exhausted mother may even encourage her young to become independent by leaving them at a den and giving them the slip for a few days so that they are forced to hunt for themselves. By the end of July the young minks' exploratory movements begin to take them beyond the limits of their mother's territory.

Most young mink disperse in search of their own territories during August, apparently as a consequence of increased intolerance by their mothers. Young females do not usually disperse very far, often settling within 5 kilometres of their place of birth; young males disperse further as a rule, commonly in excess of 10 kilometres and possibly much further. The more fortunate young mink find vacant territories in which to settle during August and September, but some are still searching for a home up to December.

Parasites and diseases

The afflictions to which ranch mink are prone, including distemper, tuberculosis, botulism, enteritis, pleurisy and Aleutian disease (to name but a few) are well known. In contrast we know little about the ailments of wild feral mink. There is an isolated report of a distemper-like disease which reduced the numbers of mink on one river in south-west England. On another river in the same area, 10 per cent of mink trapped and autopsied were found to have diseased kidneys, suggesting that renal failure might be a significant cause of mortality if this phenomenon is widespread. Several feral mink trapped and autopsied during a Swedish study were found to have gastric ulcers, and many showed signs of starvation. Feral mink are also prone to jaw abscesses, which may lead to secondary infection and death. It is possible that heavy metal pollution affects feral mink populations in some areas and significant levels of mercury have been found in the livers of Swedish mink.

Feral mink commonly carry light infestations of ticks, and occasionally fleas, none of which are apparently specific to mink. Ticks are usually found attached to the ears, head or neck but few animals carry more than half a dozen. Two species of tick have been identified from feral mink: the hedgehog tick *Ixodes hexagonus* and the sheep tick *Ixodes ricinus*. Fleas are only rarely found. At least four species have been identified, and all normally parasitise common small mammals.

Relations with Man

To many people the word 'mink' still conjures up the image of a very expensive fur coat adorning the shoulders of a wealthy woman at a society ball or film premiere. It was not until feral mink had made their presence felt in Britain that people came to associate the word primarily with the live animal and with the mischief that it was reputedly doing in the countryside.

Wild mink have been trapped for their fur for centuries, and this practice still continues in parts of North America. Some Eskimo trappers in Alaska even cook and eat mink after skinning them. Today, however, most of the demand for mink fur is satisfied by farms or ranches where mink are bred and reared in captivity. Indeed the once lucrative North American fur trapping trade has declined to the extent that most trappers now treat it as a part-time job or sideline rather than as their sole source of income.

In 1962 there were 561 registered mink farms in Britain; by 1 March 1984 there were only 54. Alongside this tenfold reduction in numbers, mink farms have become larger and more efficiently run. Most mink pelts in Britain are now produced on farms based on 1,000–2,000 breeding females. Total British pelt production in the 1983–84 pelting season was just under 95,000. World pelt production is measured in millions; Russia alone is thought to produce about 10 million pelts annually.

Whereas a good mink farmer might expect to receive around £16–£20 for each pelt, with top class specimens fetching up to £50, the fur of feral mink is almost worthless by comparison. One firm which deals in the skins of wild British mammals offered a maximum of £3 for a mink skin in 1984. There is clearly not a living to be made trapping mink in Britain.

Thousands of mink are trapped and shot in Britain each year by game-keepers, farmers, water bailiffs, angling clubs and owners of waterfowl collections. However, experience shows that eradication, even on a very local scale, is difficult to achieve.

One intensive trapping programme, on a small river system in Devon,

Opposite
Top: When swimming at the surface, a mink rides high in the water.
Bottom: Scat showing remains of prey.

involved the removal of 47 mink from 27 kilometres of river in one year. This was not enough, however, because a small number survived to form the nucleus of the next year's breeding population. Even if every mink had been trapped, recolonisation by animals from tributaries and neighbouring river systems would soon have refilled the vacant territories. Attempts to clear mink from waterways tend, therefore, to meet with only limited local and temporary success at best. It is only on those rivers with exceptionally high densities of gamekeepers and water bailiffs that effective control of mink can be achieved.

Now that the otter is protected from hunting by law in Britain, at least six otterhound packs have switched to hunting mink. In addition, several entirely new minkhound packs have been formed, so that a total of 20 packs had been registered with the Masters of Minkhounds Association by December 1984. Any unregistered packs are not bound by the constitution and rules of the Association. Most of England and all of Wales is now hunted over by registered minkhound packs; in Scotland there is some hunting in the south-west.

Mink-hunting is carried out between April and September, when rivers are safe to wade and not too cold. (Unlike most other organised fieldsports this includes the quarry's breeding season.) Hounds hunt slowly along the riverbank, exploring every likely den site for signs of occupancy by mink. A typical hunt consists of a series of short chases as the hunted mink dashes from one waterside refuge to another. Hunt servants attempt to bolt any mink which has 'gone to ground'. As many as two-thirds of mink 'found' by hounds are not killed, often because they cannot be evicted from secure refuges in rocks or under trees. Most hunts kill 40–50 mink per season. A reliable estimate of the annual nationwide total is 700–800. At this intensity, hunting is unlikely to exert a controlling influence upon mink populations. However, there is concern among conservationists that minkhunting may represent a serious disturbance to the scarce and endangered otter.

It is not difficult to see how the mink has become one of the most despised creatures in the countryside. Sadly there is still a tendency for many country people to view any predator as undesirable vermin. This prejudice has been exacerbated in the case of mink by endless xenophobic scaremongering beneath newspaper headlines like *Vicious Alien Threatens Wildlife*. Even now, over 10 years after mink had become widely established in Britain, emotive articles continue to exaggerate and sensationalise the threat which mink pose to wildlife. Yet 10 years of research in the field have revealed no evidence of the ecological disasters so often predicted in the past. The mink's unenviable reputation is largely undeserved, and perhaps, given time, we may view this vigorous little predator in a more balanced light.